West Midland Poets

Edited By Jess Giaffreda

First published in Great Britain in 2019 by:

Young Writers
Remus House
Coltsfoot Drive
Peterborough
PE2 9BF
Telephone: 01733 890066
Website: www.youngwriters.co.uk

FOREWORD

Dear Reader,

Are you ready to get your thinking caps on to puzzle your way through this wonderful collection?

Young Writers are proud to introduce our new poetry competition, *My First Riddle*, designed to introduce Reception pupils to the delights of poetry. Riddles are a great way to introduce children to the use of poetic expression, including description, similes and expanded noun phrases, as well as encouraging them to 'think outside the box' by providing clues without giving the answer away immediately. Some pupils were given a series of riddle templates to choose from, giving them a framework within which to shape their ideas.

Their answers could be whatever or whoever their imaginations desired; from people to places, animals to objects, food to seasons. All of us here at Young Writers believe in the importance of inspiring young children to produce creative writing, including poetry, and we feel that seeing their own riddles in print will ignite that spark of creativity.

We hope you enjoy riddling your way through this book as much as we enjoyed reading all the entries.

CONTENTS

Gabriel Scotto (4) 59

St Bernadette's Catholic Primary School, Birmingham

Miguel Brent Perez Dela Paz (5) 60
Louis Carson (4) 61
Jaxon Morris (5) 62
Amaya Jannat Khan (5) 63
Sienna Grace Cochrane (4) 64
Joey Walsh (5) 65
Hijab Nisa (5) 66
Artemisia Constantinou (4) 67
A'kari Terraine Wright (5) 68
Maverick Panelo (4) 69
Edward Cash (4) 70
George Beckett (5) 71
Eleanor Mia Barnsley (5) 72
Macey Michie (5) 73
Josh George (5) 74
Tafari Dryden (4) 75
Hiba Arfan (5) 76
Igor Kasperski (5) 77
Victoria Mbambu (4) 78
Maria-Eleni Panayiotou (4) 79
Olivia Hackney (5) 80
Kyle Moriarty (5) 81
Arianna Yoosuf (4) 82
Teejay Sattar (4) 83
Makeyz Sahak (4) 84
Khalil Walters (5) 85
Aliza Ali (5) 86
John-Patrick Perrigo (5) 87
Kahil Miah (5) 88
Tilleah Jones-Kinyok (5) 89
Keron Whyte (5) 90
Sonny Cooper (5) 91
Scarlett-Louise Pinches (5) 92

St Catherine Of Siena RC Primary School, Lee Bank

Judyta Gawlik (5) 93

St Francis Catholic Primary School, Bedworth

Mason Dadley (4) 94
Amelie Rose Worby (5) 95
Niamh Kincaid (4) 96
Stanley Steggall (5) 97
Daniel Bridgewater (4) 98
Ignacy Karwicki (5) 99
Alex (5) 100
Archie Lenton (4) 101
Harleigh Trevitt (5) 102
Layton Green (4) 103
Jessica Maziarz (5) 104
Chloe Staton (5) 105
James Macdonald (5) 106
Brooklyn Curran (4) 107
Austin Morgan-Blinco (5) 108
Liliana Morris (5) 109
George Plimbley (5) 110
Hugo Blakeman (4) 111
Isabella Michelle Joanne Hester (4) 112
Georgia Ann Fitzgerald (4) 113

The Coppice Primary School, Hollywood

Eva Lily Elwell (5) 114
Harper James (5) 115
Thomas Stretch (5) 116
Maeva Pampols (5) 117
Amelia Hill (4) 118
Siene Marlow McGarry (4) 119
Levi Collett (4) 120
Ellie Ryan (5) 121
Aaron Brittain (4) 122
Kesia Quaintance (5) 123
Eliana (4) 124
Emily Astle (4) 125

The Richard Heathcote Community Primary School, Alsagers Bank

Tudor Grange Primary Academy Haselor, Haselor

THE RIDDLES

Amber's First Riddle

What could it be?
Follow the clues and see.

It looks like **white, galloping horses.**
It sounds like **splashing and sploshing.**
It smells like **a holiday.**
It feels **wet and cold.**
It tastes like **salt and sand.**

Have you guessed what it could be?
Look below and you will see,
It is...

Answer: The sea's waves.

Amber Hanson (4)
Charford First School, Charford

Charlie's First Riddle

Who could it be?
Follow the clues and see.

It looks like **a little cuddly bear.**
It sounds like *woof woof!*
It smells like **muddy puddles.**
It feels **silky soft with a wet nose.**
It tastes like **hair and mud.**

Have you guessed who it could be?
Look below and you will see,
It is...

Answer: *Trigger (my dog).*

Charlie Russ Wilkinson (5)
Charford First School, Charford

Daisy's First Riddle

What could it be?
Follow the clues and see.

It looks like **a fluffy creature.**
It sounds like *boing!*
It smells like **a carrot.**
It feels like **a soft teddy.**
It tastes like **fluffy hair, carrots and lettuce.**

Have you guessed what it could be?
Look below and you will see,
It is...

Answer: A rabbit.

Daisy Taylor-Rogers (4)
Charford First School, Charford

Lily's First Riddle

What could it be?
Follow the clues and see.

It looks like **broccoli**.
It sounds like *rustle rustle*!
It smells like **sawdust**.
It feels like **wrinkly skin**.
It tastes like **fruit and leaves**.

Have you guessed what it could be?
Look below and you will see,
It is...

Answer: *A tree.*

Lily Williams (4)
Charford First School, Charford

Zavier's First Riddle

What could it be?
Follow the clues and see.

It looks **small, round and light brown.**
It sounds like *pop!*
It smells like **sweet buttered toast.**
It feels **hard and crunchy.**
It tastes **sweet or salty.**

Have you guessed what it could be?
Look below and you will see,
It is...

Answer: **Popcorn.**

Zavier Nicholls (5)
Charford First School, Charford

Miley's First Riddle

What could it be?
Follow the clues and see.

It looks like **circles or squares**.
It sounds like *munch munch*!
It smells like **vanilla**.
It feels like **sponges**.
It tastes like **jam**.

Have you guessed what it could be?
Look below and you will see,
It is...

Answer: A birthday cake.

Miley Collins (5)
Charford First School, Charford

Leo's First Riddle

What could it be?
Follow the clues and see.

It looks like **Peppa and George**.
It sounds like *oink oink!*
It smells like **mud**.
It feels **rough and hairy**.
It tastes like **sausage and bacon**.

Have you guessed what it could be?
Look below and you will see,
It is...

Answer: A pig.

Leo Byng (5)
Charford First School, Charford

Bethany's First Riddle

What could it be?
Follow the clues and see.

It looks like **orange flashes**.
It sounds like *snap, crackle, pop!*
It smells like **burning wood**.
It feels like **hot sun**.
It tastes like **smoky air**.

Have you guessed what it could be?
Look below and you will see,
It is...

Answer: Fire.

Bethany Rose Lander (4)
Charford First School, Charford

Jack's First Riddle

What could it be?
Follow the clues and see.

It looks like **a fluffy cloud.**
It sounds like **something yummy.**
It smells like **something sweet.**
It feels like **cotton wool.**
It tastes like **sugar.**

Have you guessed what it could be?
Look below and you will see,
It is...

Answer: Candyfloss.

Jack Waters (4)
Charford First School, Charford

Lucas' First Riddle

What could it be?
Follow the clues and see.

It looks like **a rocket.**
It sounds like *slurp slurp*!
It smells like **oranges.**
It feels like **snow.**
It tastes like **fruit.**

Have you guessed what it could be?
Look below and you will see,
It is...

Answer: An ice lolly.

Lucas Hadley-Blight (4)
Charford First School, Charford

Ruby's First Riddle

What could it be?
Follow the clues and see.

It looks like **it's yummy.**
It sounds like **a party!**
It smells like **delicious icing.**
It feels like **sponge.**
It tastes like **a sweet treat.**

Have you guessed what it could be?
Look below and you will see,
It is...

Answer: A cupcake.

Ruby Harrison (5)
Charford First School, Charford

Micheal's First Riddle

What could it be?
Follow the clues and see.

It looks **blue and white**.
It sounds like *roar!*
It smells like **fish**.
It feels **smooth and wet**.
It tastes like **meat**.

Have you guessed what it could be?
Look below and you will see,
It is...

Answer: A megalodon.

Micheal Smith (5)
Charford First School, Charford

Isabelle's First Riddle

What could it be?
Follow the clues and see.

It looks like **water.**
It sounds like **waves.**
It smells like **bananas.**
It feels **hot and cold.**
It tastes like **water, bananas and apples.**

Have you guessed what it could be?
Look below and you will see,
It is...

Answer: *The beach.*

Isabelle Wakefield (4)
Charford First School, Charford

Louie's First Riddle

What could it be?
Follow the clues and see.

It looks **fluffy**.
It sounds like **giggles**.
It smells like **bubblegum**.
It feels **soft and cuddly**.
It tastes like **fur**.

Have you guessed what it could be?
Look below and you will see,
It is...

Answer: My Build-A-Bear teddy.

Louie Lavin (4)
Charford First School, Charford

Louisa's First Riddle

What could it be?
Follow the clues and see.

It looks like **small rocks.**
It sounds like **popping.**
It smells like **sweet candy.**
It feels **sticky.**
It tastes like **fruit.**

Have you guessed what it could be?
Look below and you will see,
It is...

Answer: Popping candy.

Louisa Kym Morris (5)
Charford First School, Charford

Dylan's First Riddle

What could it be?
Follow the clues and see.

It looks like **a circle**.
It sounds like **yum yum**.
It smells **sweet**.
It feels like **a cushion**.
It tastes like **sugar**.

Have you guessed what it could be?
Look below and you will see,
It is...

Answer: A marshmallow.

Dylan Hussey (4)
Charford First School, Charford

Sienna-Rose's First Riddle

What could it be?
Follow the clues and see.

It looks like **squares**.
It sounds like *crack!*
It smells like **milk**.
It feels **hard**.
It tastes like **mmm**.

Have you guessed what it could be?
Look below and you will see,
It is...

Answer: Chocolate.

Sienna-Rose Kettle (5)
Charford First School, Charford

Charlie's First Riddle

What could it be?
Follow the clues and see.

It looks **pink**.
It sounds **yummy**.
It smells like **strawberry**.
It feels **freezing**.
It tastes like **ice**.

Have you guessed what it could be?
Look below and you will see,
It is...

Answer: Strawberry ice cream.

Charlie Young (5)
Charford First School, Charford

Leo's First Riddle

What could it be?
Follow the clues and see.

It looks like **four triangles**.
It sounds **crunchy**.
It smells like **cheese**.
It feels **soft**.
It tastes like **tomatoes**.

Have you guessed what it could be?
Look below and you will see,
It is...

Answer: Pizza.

Leo Hilton (5)
Charford First School, Charford

Olivia's First Riddle

What could it be?
Follow the clues and see.

It looks like **the moon**.
It sounds like **bees**.
It smells like **socks**.
It feels like **rubber**.
It tastes like **feet**.

Have you guessed what it could be?
Look below and you will see,
It is...

Answer: Cheese.

Olivia Rose Shemmans (5)
Charford First School, Charford

Alex's First Riddle

What could it be?
Follow the clues and see.

It looks like **the same colour as an orange.**
It sounds like *crunch crunch!*
It smells **really nice.**
It feels **cold.**
It tastes **yummy.**

Have you guessed what it could be?
Look below and you will see,
It is...

Answer: A carrot.

Alex Lockley (5)
Moat Hall Primary School, Great Wyrley

Corey's First Riddle

What could it be?
Follow the clues and see.

It looks like **small, bumpy balls.**
It sounds like *pop, crunch crunch*!
It smells like **toffee.**
It feels like **bumps.**
It tastes like **sugar.**

Have you guessed what it could be?
Look below and you will see,
It is...

Answer: Popcorn.

Corey Bevan (4)
Moat Hall Primary School, Great Wyrley

Dana's First Riddle

What could it be?
Follow the clues and see.

It looks like **a fluffy tail**.
It sounds like ***woof woof!***
It smells like **mud**.
It feels like **a fluffy teddy**.
It tastes like **a bone**.

Have you guessed what it could be?
Look below and you will see,
It is...

Answer: A dog.

Dana Thompson Dias (5)
Moat Hall Primary School, Great Wyrley

Noah's First Riddle

What could it be?
Follow the clues and see.

It looks like **two wheels and a handlebar**.
It sounds like *vroom vroom*!
It smells like **diesel**.
It feels **smooth**.
It tastes like **gas**.

Have you guessed what it could be?
Look below and you will see,
It is...

Answer: A motorbike.

Noah Beech (4)
Moat Hall Primary School, Great Wyrley

Hayden's First Riddle

What could it be?
Follow the clues and see.

It looks **dark green**.
It sounds like *splash splash!*
It smells like **the sea**.
It feels like **scales**.
It tastes like **salt**.

Have you guessed what it could be?
Look below and you will see,
It is...

Answer: A fish.

Hayden Marlow (5)
Moat Hall Primary School, Great Wyrley

Hannah's First Riddle

What could it be?
Follow the clues and see.

It looks **beautiful**.
It sounds like *singing*!
It smells like **flowers**.
It feels **soft**.
It tastes like **sprinkles and glitter**.

Have you guessed what it could be?
Look below and you will see,
It is...

Answer: A princess.

Hannah King (4)
Moat Hall Primary School, Great Wyrley

Bonnie's First Riddle

What could it be?
Follow the clues and see.

It looks like **a white fluffy ball.**
It sounds like *boing!*
It smells like **carrots.**
It feels **soft.**
It tastes like **rabbit food.**

Have you guessed what it could be?
Look below and you will see,
It is...

Answer: A bunny.

Bonnie Severn (5)
Moat Hall Primary School, Great Wyrley

Joseph's First Riddle

What could it be?
Follow the clues and see.

It looks like **big ears and a stretched face.**
It sounds like **eee-ooor.**
It smells like **the farm.**
It feels **fluffy.**
It tastes like **hay.**

Have you guessed what it could be?
Look below and you will see,
It is...

Answer: A donkey.

Joseph Parr (5)
Moat Hall Primary School, Great Wyrley

Charlie's First Riddle

What could it be?
Follow the clues and see.

It looks like **a waggy tail**.
It sounds like *woof!*
It smells like **mud and grass**.
It feels like **soft fur**.
It tastes like **bones**.

Have you guessed what it could be?
Look below and you will see,
It is...

Answer: A dog.

Charlie Athersmith (5)
Moat Hall Primary School, Great Wyrley

Olivia's First Riddle

What could it be?
Follow the clues and see.

It looks like **a sausage**.
It sounds like ***woof woof***!
It smells **yucky**.
It feels **soft and furry**.
It tastes like **dirt**.

Have you guessed what it could be?
Look below and you will see,
It is...

Answer: A dog.

Olivia Horley (4)
Moat Hall Primary School, Great Wyrley

Finley's First Riddle

What could it be?
Follow the clues and see.

It looks like **brown fur**.
It sounds like ***oooh-oooh aah-aah***!
It smells like **trees**.
It feels **soft**.
It tastes like **bananas**.

Have you guessed what it could be?
Look below and you will see,
It is...

Answer: A monkey.

Finley Ward (4)
Moat Hall Primary School, Great Wyrley

Skylar-Ellen's First Riddle

What could it be?
Follow the clues and see.

It looks like **a horn**.
It sounds like **a horse when it neighs**.
It smells **yummy**.
It feels like **soft fur**.
It tastes like **chips**.

Have you guessed what it could be?
Look below and you will see,
It is...

Answer: A unicorn.

Skylar-Ellen Okell (4)
Moat Hall Primary School, Great Wyrley

Madeline's First Riddle

What could it be?
Follow the clues and see.

It looks like **a horse**.
It sounds like **music**.
It smells like **sweets**.
It feels like **a fluffy horse**.
It tastes like **rainbows**.

Have you guessed what it could be?
Look below and you will see,
It is...

Answer: A unicorn.

Madeline Turner-Wilkes (5)
Moat Hall Primary School, Great Wyrley

Harper-Rae's First Riddle

What could it be?
Follow the clues and see.

It looks like **big, pink ears.**
It sounds like **hopping.**
It smells **really good.**
It feels **soft.**
It tastes like **carrots.**

Have you guessed what it could be?
Look below and you will see,
It is...

Answer: A bunny rabbit.

Harper-Rae Collins (4)
Moat Hall Primary School, Great Wyrley

Lexie-Mae's First Riddle

What could it be?
Follow the clues and see.

It looks like **a fluffy tail**.
It sounds like *boing*!
It smells like **mud**.
It feels **fluffy**.
It tastes like **carrots**.

Have you guessed what it could be?
Look below and you will see,
It is...

Answer: A rabbit.

Lexie-Mae Davis (4)
Moat Hall Primary School, Great Wyrley

Lily-Ann's First Riddle

What could it be?
Follow the clues and see.

It looks like **a long horn**.
It sounds like **music**.
It smells like **flowers**.
It feels like **soft fur**.
It tastes like **sweets**.

Have you guessed what it could be?
Look below and you will see,
It is...

Answer: A unicorn.

Lily-Ann Garbett (5)
Moat Hall Primary School, Great Wyrley

Jake's First Riddle

What could it be?
Follow the clues and see.

It looks **big**.
It sounds like *wheee!*
It smells like **a playground**.
It feels **hard**.
It tastes like **metal**.

Have you guessed what it could be?
Look below and you will see,
It is...

Answer: A slide.

Jake Evans (4)
Moat Hall Primary School, Great Wyrley

Keyaan's First Riddle

What could it be?
Follow the clues and see.

It looks **brown and white**.
It sounds like **growling**.
It smells like **dirt**.
It feels like **a furry tail**.
It tastes **disgusting**.

Have you guessed what it could be?
Look below and you will see,
It is...

Answer: A fox.

Keyaan Rashid (4)
Moat Hall Primary School, Great Wyrley

Dario's First Riddle

What could it be?
Follow the clues and see.

It looks like **black legs**.
It sounds **quiet**.
It smells like **spiderwebs**.
It feels like **soft fur**.
It tastes **disgusting**.

Have you guessed what it could be?
Look below and you will see,
It is...

Answer: A spider.

Dario Careaga (4)
Moat Hall Primary School, Great Wyrley

Georgie's First Riddle

What could it be?
Follow the clues and see.

It looks like **a rainbow**.
It sounds like **a song**.
It smells like **flowers**.
It feels **soft**.
It tastes like **sweeties**.

Have you guessed what it could be?
Look below and you will see,
It is...

Answer: A princess.

Georgie Powell (5)
Moat Hall Primary School, Great Wyrley

Mollie's First Riddle

What could it be?
Follow the clues and see.

It looks **black**.
It sounds like **ooooh!**
It smells like **grass**.
It feels **soft**.
It tastes **not nice**.

Have you guessed what it could be?
Look below and you will see,
It is...

Answer: *The dark.*

Mollie Freeman (5)
Moat Hall Primary School, Great Wyrley

Farah's First Riddle

What could it be?
Follow the clues and see.

It looks like **a big red and green ball**.
It sounds like **a piece of wood**.
It smells like **a piece of fruit**.
It feels **hard**.
It tastes **sweet and fruity**.

Have you guessed what it could be?
Look below and you will see,
It is...

Answer: An apple.

Farah Ames-Leech (5)
Nathaniel Newton Infant School, Hartshill

Declan's First Riddle

What could it be?
Follow the clues and see.

It looks like **a green leaf**.
It sounds like **crunch**!
It smells like **a strawberry**.
It feels **wet and squashy**.
It tastes **yummy and juicy**.

Have you guessed what it could be?
Look below and you will see,
It is...

Answer: A strawberry.

Declan Haddon (5)
Nathaniel Newton Infant School, Hartshill

Lily's First Riddle

What could it be?
Follow the clues and see.

It looks like **the moon.**
It sounds like **a crunch.**
It smells like **fruit.**
It feels **soft and smooth.**
It tastes like **a monkey's snack.**

Have you guessed what it could be?
Look below and you will see,
It is...

Answer: A banana.

Lily Stockton (5)
Nathaniel Newton Infant School, Hartshill

Jack's First Riddle

What could it be?
Follow the clues and see.

It looks like **clouds**.
It sounds like *pop pop pop!*
It smells like **salt**.
It feels **bumpy**.
It tastes **good, salty and buttery**.

Have you guessed what it could be?
Look below and you will see,
It is...

Answer: Popcorn.

Jack Abbott (5)
Nathaniel Newton Infant School, Hartshill

Noah's First Riddle

What could it be?
Follow the clues and see.

It looks **green and brown.**
It sounds like **a bounce.**
It smells like **apples.**
It feels **tickly and hairy.**
It tastes **yummy and sour.**

Have you guessed what it could be?
Look below and you will see,
It is...

Answer: A kiwi!

Noah James Temple (4)
Nathaniel Newton Infant School, Hartshill

Zaynah's First Riddle

What could it be?
Follow the clues and see.

It looks like **lots of clouds**.
It sounds like *pop pop pop!*
It smells like **butter**.
It feels **bumpy**.
It tastes **salty**.

Have you guessed what it could be?
Look below and you will see,
It is...

Answer: Popcorn.

Zaynah Taylor (4)
Nathaniel Newton Infant School, Hartshill

Jack's First Riddle

What could it be?
Follow the clues and see.

It looks like **broken crisps**.
It sounds like **crunch**!
It smells like **caramel**.
It feels **soft**.
It tastes like **crunch**.

Have you guessed what it could be?
Look below and you will see,
It is...

Answer: Popcorn.

Jack Thomason (5)
Nathaniel Newton Infant School, Hartshill

Elena's First Riddle

What could it be?
Follow the clues and see.

It looks like **a snowman's body**.
It sounds like **crunch**!
It smells **smelly**.
It feels **big and soft**.
It tastes **juicy**.

Have you guessed what it could be?
Look below and you will see,
It is...

Answer: An orange.

Elena Irene Belcher (4)
Nathaniel Newton Infant School, Hartshill

Jayden's First Riddle

What could it be?
Follow the clues and see.

It looks **green**.
It sounds like **crack**!
It smells like **a strawberry**.
It feels like **a face**.
It tastes like **mint**.

Have you guessed what it could be?
Look below and you will see,
It is...

Answer: A strawberry.

Jayden Macca (4)
Nathaniel Newton Infant School, Hartshill

Leila's First Riddle

What could it be?
Follow the clues and see.

It looks like **a big orange**.
It sounds **quiet**.
It smells like **oranges**.
It feels **bumpy**.
It tastes **juicy**.

Have you guessed what it could be?
Look below and you will see,
It is...

Answer: An orange.

Leila Amelia Dick (4)
Nathaniel Newton Infant School, Hartshill

Emily's First Riddle

What could it be?
Follow the clues and see.

It looks like **an acorn**.
It sounds **quiet**.
It smells **sweet**.
It feels **bumpy**.
It tastes **juicy**.

Have you guessed what it could be?
Look below and you will see,
It is...

Answer: A strawberry.

Emily Holden (5)
Nathaniel Newton Infant School, Hartshill

Mia-Jade's First Riddle

What could it be?
Follow the clues and see.

It looks **white**.
It sounds like *pop!*
It smells **sweet**.
It feels **soft**.
It tastes **sweet**.

Have you guessed what it could be?
Look below and you will see,
It is...

Answer: Popcorn.

Mia-Jade Holcroft (4)
Nathaniel Newton Infant School, Hartshill

Riley's First Riddle

What could it be?
Follow the clues and see.

It looks like **an egg**.
It sounds **quiet**.
It smells **sweet**.
It feels **spiky**.
It tastes **juicy**.

Have you guessed what it could be?
Look below and you will see,
It is...

Answer: A kiwi.

Riley Pearce (5)
Nathaniel Newton Infant School, Hartshill

Harrison's First Riddle

What could it be?
Follow the clues and see.

It looks like **a bumblebee**.
It sounds like *tap tap!*
It smells like **fresh wood**.
It feels like **tree sticks**.
It tastes like **wood**.

Have you guessed what it could be?
Look below and you will see,
It is...

Answer: A yellow and black writing pencil.

Harrison Merrett (5)
Packwood Haugh School, Shrewsbury

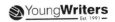

Albert's First Riddle

What could it be?
Follow the clues and see.

It looks like **a witch's broom.**
It sounds like *splash splash!*
It smells like **cleaning.**
It feels like **floppy wet hair.**
It tastes like **sloppy soup.**

Have you guessed what it could be?
Look below and you will see,
It is...

Answer: A mop.

Albert Woollam (5)
Packwood Haugh School, Shrewsbury

Peter's First Riddle

What could it be?
Follow the clues and see.

It looks like **branches all together**.
It sounds like *snap snap!*
It smells like **bark**.
It feels **hard and bumpy**.
It tastes **crunchy**.

Have you guessed what it could be?
Look below and you will see,
It is...

Answer: *A tree.*

Peter Christensen (4)
Packwood Haugh School, Shrewsbury

Alexander's First Riddle

What could it be?
Follow the clues and see.

It looks **big**.
It sounds like ***brum brum***!
It smells like **grass**.
It feels like **dirt**.
It tastes like **mud**.

Have you guessed what it could be?
Look below and you will see,
It is...

Answer: A tractor.

Alexander Blackwood (4)
Packwood Haugh School, Shrewsbury

Gabriel's First Riddle

What could it be?
Follow the clues and see.

It looks like **fingers and a face**.
It sounds like **tick-tock**.
It smells like **metal**.
It feels like **a pyjama cuff**.
It tastes **hard and crunchy**.

Have you guessed what it could be?
Look below and you will see,
It is...

Answer: A watch.

Gabriel Scotto (4)
Packwood Haugh School, Shrewsbury

Miguel's First Riddle

What could it be?
Follow the clues and see.

It looks like **a giant pet**.
It sounds like *roar, stomp* and *chomp*!
It smells like **leaves and dirt on earth**.
It feels like a **sharp and tough rock**.
It tastes like **the meat you eat**.

Have you guessed what it could be?
Look below and you will see,
It is...

Answer: A dinosaur.

Miguel Brent Perez Dela Paz (5)
St Bernadette's Catholic Primary School,
Birmingham

Louis' First Riddle

What could it be?
Follow the clues and see.

It looks like **a round circle**.
It sounds like *crunch crunch*!
It smells like **yummy chocolate**.
It feels like **bumpy crumbs**.
It tastes like **delicious chocolate**.

Have you guessed what it could be?
Look below and you will see,
It is...

Answer: A cookie.

Louis Carson (4)

St Bernadette's Catholic Primary School,
Birmingham

Jaxon's First Riddle

What could it be?
Follow the clues and see.

It looks like **a cloud of white fluff.**
It sounds like **a lion roaring.**
It smells like **a big wet dog.**
It feels like **a fluffy teddy bear.**
It tastes like... **we hope no one knows.**

Have you guessed what it could be?
Look below and you will see,
It is...

Answer: A polar bear.

Jaxon Morris (5)
St Bernadette's Catholic Primary School,
Birmingham

Amaya's First Riddle

What could it be?
Follow the clues and see.

It looks like **black and yellow stripes**.
It sounds like *buzz buzz!*
It smells like **pretty flowers**.
It feels like **fur**.
It tastes like **sweet honey**.

Have you guessed what it could be?
Look below and you will see,
It is...

Answer: A bumblebee.

Amaya Jannat Khan (5)
St Bernadette's Catholic Primary School,
Birmingham

Sienna's First Riddle

What could it be?
Follow the clues and see.

It looks like **a pom-pom**.
It sounds like *thump thump!*
It smells like **fresh straw**.
It feels like **cotton wool**.
It tastes like **carrots and lettuce**.

Have you guessed what it could be?
Look below and you will see,
It is...

Answer: A rabbit.

Sienna Grace Cochrane (4)
St Bernadette's Catholic Primary School,
Birmingham

Joey's First Riddle

What could it be?
Follow the clues and see.

It looks like **it's round but doesn't roll.**
It sounds like **it will smash if you drop it.**
It smells like **pink custard.**
It feels **hard.**
It tastes like **sweeties.**

Have you guessed what it could be?
Look below and you will see,
It is...

Answer: A lollipop.

Joey Walsh (5)
St Bernadette's Catholic Primary School,
Birmingham

Hijab's First Riddle

What could it be?
Follow the clues and see.

It looks like **four wooden rectangles**.
It sounds like **slapping your hand on wood**.
It smells like **old, dirty wood**.
It feels like **hard wood**.
It tastes like **dried wood**.

Have you guessed what it could be?
Look below and you will see,
It is...

Answer: A cupboard.

Hijab Nisa (5)
St Bernadette's Catholic Primary School,
Birmingham

Artemisia's First Riddle

What could it be?
Follow the clues and see.

It looks **white and yellow**.
It sounds like *crunch crunch!*
It smells **sweet and salty**.
It feels **soft and spiky**.
It tastes like **good sweets**.

Have you guessed what it could be?
Look below and you will see,
It is...

Answer: **Popcorn.**

Artemisia Constantinou (4)
St Bernadette's Catholic Primary School,
Birmingham

A'kari's First Riddle

What could it be?
Follow the clues and see.

It looks like **a small tree branch**.
It sounds like *scribble scrabble!*
It smells like **wood and graphite**.
It feels like **plastic**.
It tastes like **dirt**.

Have you guessed what it could be?
Look below and you will see,
It is...

Answer: A pencil.

A'kari Terraine Wright (5)
St Bernadette's Catholic Primary School,
Birmingham

Maverick's First Riddle

What could it be?
Follow the clues and see.

It looks like **a crunchy crystal**.
It sounds like **a cool musical**.
It smells like **an ice lolly**.
It feels **fluffy and sticky**.
It tastes like **a slushy shake**.

Have you guessed what it could be?
Look below and you will see,
It is...

Answer: A snowflake.

Maverick Panelo (4)
St Bernadette's Catholic Primary School,
Birmingham

Ned's First Riddle

What could they be?
Follow the clues and see.

They look like **brown sticks**.
They sound like **sizzling in a pan**.
They smell **yummy and nice**.
They feel **soft like a pillow**.
They taste **yummy and nice**.

Have you guessed what they could be?
Look below and you will see,
They are...

Answer: Sausages.

Edward Cash (4)
St Bernadette's Catholic Primary School,
Birmingham

George's First Riddle

What could it be?
Follow the clues and see.

It looks like **a square**.
It sounds like *zip zip!*
It smells like **leather**.
It feels **soft**.
It tastes like... **you wouldn't eat it.**

Have you guessed what it could be?
Look below and you will see,
It is...

Answer: A bag.

George Beckett (5)
St Bernadette's Catholic Primary School,
Birmingham

Eleanor's First Riddle

What could it be?
Follow the clues and see.

It looks like **a tiger, orange and stripy.**
It sounds like **a horse puffing.**
It smells like **straw in a barn.**
It feels **soft and cosy.**
It tastes like **marmalade.**

Have you guessed what it could be?
Look below and you will see,
It is...

Answer: A cat.

Eleanor Mia Barnsley (5)
St Bernadette's Catholic Primary School,
Birmingham

Macey's First Riddle

What could it be?
Follow the clues and see.

It looks like **tiny blue drops**.
It sounds like *pitter-patter!*
It smells like **fresh air**.
It feels like **a cold, wet shower**.
It tastes like **water**.

Have you guessed what it could be?
Look below and you will see,
It is...

Answer: *Rain.*

Macey Michie (5)
St Bernadette's Catholic Primary School,
Birmingham

Josh's First Riddle

What could it be?
Follow the clues and see.

It looks like **a human**.
It sounds like **ooo-aaah**!
It smells like **a tree**.
It feels **soft**.
It tastes like **a banana**.

Have you guessed what it could be?
Look below and you will see,
It is...

Answer: A monkey.

Josh George (5)
St Bernadette's Catholic Primary School,
Birmingham

Tafari's First Riddle

What could it be?
Follow the clues and see.

It looks like **a cone**.
It sounds like ***slurp slurp!***
It smells like **cream**.
It feels like **ice**.
It tastes like **chocolate sprinkles**.

Have you guessed what it could be?
Look below and you will see,
It is...

Answer: Ice cream.

Tafari Dryden (4)
St Bernadette's Catholic Primary School,
Birmingham

Hiba's First Riddle

What could it be?
Follow the clues and see.

It looks like **a cat that likes water**.
It sounds like *woof woof!*
It smells like **muddy mud**.
It feels **soft**.
It tastes like **fear**.

Have you guessed what it could be?
Look below and you will see,
It is...

Answer: A dog.

Hiba Arfan (5)
St Bernadette's Catholic Primary School,
Birmingham

Igor's First Riddle

What could it be?
Follow the clues and see.

It looks like **a small, white ball with long ears.**
It sounds like *rabbit-rabbit!*
It smells like **fresh carrot.**
It feels like **a furry ball.**

Have you guessed what it could be?
Look below and you will see,
It is...

Answer: A rabbit.

Igor Kasperski (5)
St Bernadette's Catholic Primary School,
Birmingham

Victoria's First Riddle

What could it be?
Follow the clues and see.

It looks like **four cold triangles**.
It sounds like **masticating**.
It smells like **perfume**.
It tastes like **sweets**.

Have you guessed what it could be?
Look below and you will see,
It is...

Answer: Pizza.

Victoria Mbambu (4)

St Bernadette's Catholic Primary School,
Birmingham

Maria-Eleni's First Riddle

What could it be?
Follow the clues and see.

It looks like **a fairy and an angel**.
It sounds like **a flutter**.
It smells like **flowers**.
It feels like **soft paper**.
It tastes like **water**.

Have you guessed what it could be?
Look below and you will see,
It is...

Answer: A **butterfly**.

Maria-Eleni Panayiotou (4)
St Bernadette's Catholic Primary School,
Birmingham

Olivia's First Riddle

Who could they be?
Follow the clues and see.

They look like **fluffy socks**.
They sound like *meow*!
They smell like **food**.
They feel **soft and cuddly**.
They taste **furry**.

Have you guessed who they could be?
Look below and you will see,
They are...

Answer: My kittens.

Olivia Hackney (5)
St Bernadette's Catholic Primary School,
Birmingham

Kyle's First Riddle

What could it be?
Follow the clues and see.

It looks like **a ring**.
It sounds like **a telephone**.
It smells like **a strawberry**.
It feels like **jelly**.
It tastes like **sweeties**.

Have you guessed what it could be?
Look below and you will see,
It is...

Answer: A Haribo sweet.

Kyle Moriarty (5)
St Bernadette's Catholic Primary School,
Birmingham

Arianna's First Riddle

What could it be?
Follow the clues and see.

It looks like **an animal**.
It sounds like **it's snoring**.
It smells like **stinky socks**.
It feels **warm and cosy**.
It tastes like **bacon**.

Have you guessed what it could be?
Look below and you will see,
It is...

Answer: A pig.

Arianna Yoosuf (4)

St Bernadette's Catholic Primary School,
Birmingham

Teejay's First Riddle

What could it be?
Follow the clues and see.

It looks like **a ball of fluff**.
It sounds like **sunny**.
It smells like **chocolate**.
It feels **fluffy**.
It tastes **yummy**.

Have you guessed what it could be?
Look below and you will see,
It is...

Answer: A chocolate Easter bunny.

Teejay Sattar (4)
St Bernadette's Catholic Primary School,
Birmingham

Makeyz's First Riddle

What could it be?
Follow the clues and see.

It looks like **colours**.
It sounds like **money**.
It smells like **chocolate coins**.
It feels like **magic**.
It tastes like **chocolate**.

Have you guessed what it could be?
Look below and you will see,
It is...

Answer: A rainbow.

Makeyz Sahak (4)
St Bernadette's Catholic Primary School,
Birmingham

84

Khalil's First Riddle

What could it be?
Follow the clues and see.

It looks like **a big lizard**.
It sounds like **a lion**.
It smells like **a zoo**.
It feels like **a hard shell**.
It tastes like **meat**.

Have you guessed what it could be?
Look below and you will see,
It is...

Answer: A dinosaur.

Khalil Walters (5)

St Bernadette's Catholic Primary School,
Birmingham

Aliza's First Riddle

What could it be?
Follow the clues and see.

It looks like **a daffodil**.
It sounds like **buzz**.
It smells like **honey**.
It feels **stingy**.
It tastes like **porridge**.

Have you guessed what it could be?
Look below and you will see,
It is...

Answer: A bee.

Aliza Ali (5)
St Bernadette's Catholic Primary School,
Birmingham

John-Patrick's First Riddle

What could it be?
Follow the clues and see.

It looks like **a fluffy teddy**.
It sounds like **purring**.
It smells like **milk**.
It feels like **soft hair**.
It tastes like **fur**.

Have you guessed what it could be?
Look below and you will see,
It is...

Answer: A cat.

John-Patrick Perrigo (5)
St Bernadette's Catholic Primary School,
Birmingham

Kahil's First Riddle

What could it be?
Follow the clues and see.

It looks like **a worm**.
It sounds like **sss**!
It smells like **venom**.
It feels like **leather**.
It tastes like **meat**.

Have you guessed what it could be?
Look below and you will see,
It is...

Answer: A snake.

Kahil Miah (5)
St Bernadette's Catholic Primary School,
Birmingham

Tilleah's First Riddle

What could it be?
Follow the clues and see.

It looks like **a yellow square**.
It sounds like **bees**.
It smells like **feet**.
It feels like **rubber**.
It tastes **yum yum**.

Have you guessed what it could be?
Look below and you will see,
It is...

Answer: Cheese.

Tilleah Jones-Kinyok (5)
St Bernadette's Catholic Primary School,
Birmingham

Keron's First Riddle

What could it be?
Follow the clues and see.

It looks like **gravel**.
It sounds like *crunch*!
It smells like **corn**.
It feels like **foam**.
It tastes **sweet**.

Have you guessed what it could be?
Look below and you will see,
It is...

Answer: Popcorn.

Keron Whyte (5)
St Bernadette's Catholic Primary School,
Birmingham

Sonny's First Riddle

What could it be?
Follow the clues and see.

It looks like **clouds**.
It sounds **silent**.
It smells **sweet**.
It feels **soft and fluffy**.
It tastes like **sugar**.

Have you guessed what it could be?
Look below and you will see,
It is...

Answer: Candyfloss.

Sonny Cooper (5)
St Bernadette's Catholic Primary School,
Birmingham

Scarlett-Louise's First Riddle

What could it be?
Follow the clues and see.

It looks like **a little ball**.
It smells like **fresh fruit**.
It feels **hard**.
It tastes **sweet**.

Have you guessed what it could be?
Look below and you will see,
It is...

Answer: An apple.

Scarlett-Louise Pinches (5)

St Bernadette's Catholic Primary School,
Birmingham

Judyta's First Riddle

What could it be?
Follow the clues and see.

It looks like **a tiny house.**
It sounds like **a song of the sea.**
It feels like **the bark of the tree.**
It tastes like **salty peas.**

Have you guessed what it could be?
Look below and you will see,
It is...

Answer: A seashell.

Judyta Gawlik (5)
St Catherine Of Siena RC Primary School, Lee Bank

Mason's First Riddle

What could it be?
Follow the clues and see.

It looks like **whatever is in your imagination.**
It sounds like **squelching wellies on a
rainy day.**
It smells like **plastic.**
It feels like **ice until it warms up in your
hands and becomes soft.**
It tastes like **salt, but I wouldn't eat it if I
were you!**

Have you guessed what it could be?
Look below and you will see,
It is...

Answer: Play dough.

Mason Dadley (4)
St Francis Catholic Primary School, Bedworth

Amelie's First Riddle

What could it be?
Follow the clues and see.

It looks like **a scaly mountain**.
It sounds like **a fighter jet**.
It smells like **stinky breath**.
It feels like **a cheese grater**.
It tastes like... **are you joking? You can't buy it in the shops!**

Have you guessed what it could be?
Look below and you will see,
It is...

Answer: A dinosaur.

Amelie Rose Worby (5)
St Francis Catholic Primary School, Bedworth

Niamh's First Riddle

What could it be?
Follow the clues and see.

It looks like **a big rock**.
It sounds like **a nice dream**.
It smells like **tasty sweets**.
It feels like **a winter's day**.
It tastes like **the best thing ever**.

Have you guessed what it could be?
Look below and you will see,
It is...

Answer: Ice cream.

Niamh Kincaid (4)
St Francis Catholic Primary School, Bedworth

Stanley's First Riddle

Who could they be?
Follow the clues and see.

They look like **me**.
They sound like **laughter**.
They smell like **worms**.
They feel like **happiness**.
They taste like **birthday cake**.

Have you guessed who they could be?
Look below and you will see,
They are...

Answer: My school friends.

Stanley Steggall (5)
St Francis Catholic Primary School, Bedworth

Daniel's First Riddle

What could it be?
Follow the clues and see.

It looks like **a feather**.
It sounds like **a butterfly fluttering**.
It smells like **Christmas**.
It feels like **cotton wool**.
It tastes like **water**.

Have you guessed what it could be?
Look below and you will see,
It is...

Answer: Snow.

Daniel Bridgewater (4)
St Francis Catholic Primary School, Bedworth

Ignacy's First Riddle

What could it be?
Follow the clues and see.

It looks **orange and small in a box.**
It sounds like **crackling.**
It smells like **honey.**
It feels **hard.**
It tastes like **honey and milk.**

Have you guessed what it could be?
Look below and you will see,
It is...

Answer: Cereal.

Ignacy Karwicki (5)
St Francis Catholic Primary School, Bedworth

Alex's First Riddle

What could it be?
Follow the clues and see.

It looks like **a black rectangle**.
It sounds like **rain falling**.
It smells like **wood**.
It feels **bumpy**.
It tastes like **nothing**.

Have you guessed what it could be?
Look below and you will see,
It is...

Answer: A domino.

Alex (5)
St Francis Catholic Primary School, Bedworth

Archie's First Riddle

What could it be?
Follow the clues and see.

It looks like **a white blanket**.
It sounds **crunchy**.
It smells **clean and fresh**.
It feels like **ice**.
It tastes like **a Slush Puppie**.

Have you guessed what it could be?
Look below and you will see,
It is...

Answer: *Snow.*

Archie Lenton (4)
St Francis Catholic Primary School, Bedworth

Harleigh's First Riddle

What could it be?
Follow the clues and see.

It looks like **fluff**.
It sounds like *crunch!*
It smells like **carrots**.
It feels like **ice**.
It tastes like **water**.

Have you guessed what it could be?
Look below and you will see,
It is...

Answer: A snowman.

Harleigh Trevitt (5)
St Francis Catholic Primary School, Bedworth

Layton's First Riddle

What could it be?
Follow the clues and see.

It looks like **a cat**.
It sounds like **a bear**.
It smells like **a jungle**.
It feels like **a dog**.
It tastes like **a kiwi skin**.

Have you guessed what it could be?
Look below and you will see,
It is...

Answer: A lion.

Layton Green (4)
St Francis Catholic Primary School, Bedworth

Jessica's First Riddle

What could it be?
Follow the clues and see.

It looks like **a ball.**
It sounds like **a drum.**
It smells like **a flower.**
It feels **smooth.**
It tastes **sweet and juicy.**

Have you guessed what it could be?
Look below and you will see,
It is...

Answer: An apple.

Jessica Maziarz (5)
St Francis Catholic Primary School, Bedworth

Chloe's First Riddle

What could it be?
Follow the clues and see.

It looks like **a ball of ice**.
It sounds like **drips**.
It smells **fresh**.
It feels **so soft**.
It tastes like **ice cubes**.

Have you guessed what it could be?
Look below and you will see,
It is...

Answer: A snowman.

Chloe Staton (5)
St Francis Catholic Primary School, Bedworth

James' First Riddle

What could it be?
Follow the clues and see.

It looks like **a man**.
It sounds like **it crunches**.
It smells like **fresh air**.
It feels **cold**.
It tastes like **ice**.

Have you guessed what it could be?
Look below and you will see,
It is...

Answer: A snowman.

James Macdonald (5)
St Francis Catholic Primary School, Bedworth

Brooklyn's First Riddle

What could it be?
Follow the clues and see.

It looks like **white balls**.
It sounds **silent**.
It smells like **ice**.
It feels like **snow**.
It tastes like **slush**.

Have you guessed what it could be?
Look below and you will see,
It is...

Answer: A snowman.

Brooklyn Curran (4)
St Francis Catholic Primary School, Bedworth

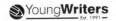

Austin's First Riddle

What could it be?
Follow the clues and see.

It looks like **a roundabout**.
It sounds **squishy**.
It smells **sweet**.
It feels like **a sponge**.
It tastes **yummy**.

Have you guessed what it could be?
Look below and you will see,
It is...

Answer: A doughnut.

Austin Morgan-Blinco (5)
St Francis Catholic Primary School, Bedworth

Liliana's First Riddle

What could it be?
Follow the clues and see.

It looks like **a man**.
It sounds **crisp**.
It smells like **a carrot**.
It feels like **ice**.
It tastes like **water**.

Have you guessed what it could be?
Look below and you will see,
It is...

Answer: A snowman.

Liliana Morris (5)
St Francis Catholic Primary School, Bedworth

YoungWriters
Est. 1991

George's First Riddle

What could it be?
Follow the clues and see.

It looks like **an alien**.
It sounds like **a Muppet**.
It smells **damp**.
It feels **slimy**.
It tastes like **chicken**.

Have you guessed what it could be?
Look below and you will see,
It is...

Answer: A frog.

George Plimbley (5)
St Francis Catholic Primary School, Bedworth

Hugo's First Riddle

What could it be?
Follow the clues and see.

It looks like **a frisbee**.
It smells like **melted cheese**.
It feels like **hot bread**.
It tastes like **tasty food**.

Have you guessed what it could be?
Look below and you will see,
It is...

Answer: **Pizza**.

Hugo Blakeman (4)
St Francis Catholic Primary School, Bedworth

Isabella's First Riddle

What could it be?
Follow the clues and see.

It looks like **sweets**.
It smells like **strawberries**.
It feels **squishy**.
It tastes **yummy**.

Have you guessed what it could be?
Look below and you will see,
It is...

Answer: Haribo.

Isabella Michelle Joanne Hester (4)
St Francis Catholic Primary School, Bedworth

Georgia's First Riddle

What could it be?
Follow the clues and see.

It looks like **an animal**.
It sounds like *roar!*
It feels **fluffy and furry**.

Have you guessed what it could be?
Look below and you will see,
It is...

Answer: A teddy bear.

Georgia Ann Fitzgerald (4)
St Francis Catholic Primary School, Bedworth

Eva's First Riddle

What could they be?
Follow the clues and see.

They look like **a walking stick.**
They sound like **crunching when you eat them.**
They smell like **mint.**
They feel **hard and sticky.**
They taste like **Christmas because we have them at Christmas at Uncle Roger's.**

Have you guessed what they could be?
Look below and you will see,
They are...

Answer: Candy canes.

Eva Lily Elwell (5)
The Coppice Primary School, Hollywood

Harper's First Riddle

What could it be?
Follow the clues and see.

It looks like **an inflatable pulled by a boat.**
It sounds like **a zoo animal called a llama.**
It smells like **a flavoured milkshake.**
It feels like **cucumber, soft and smooth.**
It tastes like **sweets made of foam.**

Have you guessed what it could be?
Look below and you will see,
It is...

Answer: A banana.

Harper James (5)
The Coppice Primary School, Hollywood

Thomas' First Riddle

What could it be?
Follow the clues and see.

It looks like **a white, fluffy cloud**.
It sounds like **a quiet mouse**.
It smells like **sweet perfume**.
It feels like **a squishy, soft ball**.
It tastes like **a sweet, delicious cloud**.

Have you guessed what it could be?
Look below and you will see,
It is...

Answer: A marshmallow.

Thomas Stretch (5)
The Coppice Primary School, Hollywood

Maeva's First Riddle

What could it be?
Follow the clues and see.

It looks like **a silly cylinder**.
It sounds like **sizzling pops and bangs**.
It smells like **breakfast is ready**.
It feels like **something squishy**.
It tastes like **heaven**.

Have you guessed what it could be?
Look below and you will see,
It is...

Answer: A sausage.

Maeva Pampols (5)
The Coppice Primary School, Hollywood

Amelia's First Riddle

What could it be?
Follow the clues and see.

It looks like **grains of yellow rice**.
It sounds like **popping**.
It smells like **delicious cereals**.
It feels like **smooth pebbles**.
It tastes like **yummy cereals**.

Have you guessed what it could be?
Look below and you will see,
It is...

Answer: *Rice Krispies*.

Amelia Hill (4)
The Coppice Primary School, Hollywood

Siene's First Riddle

What could it be?
Follow the clues and see.

It looks like **it's shiny and tempting**.
It sounds like **popping**.
It smells like **toffee**.
It feels **crunchy**.
It tastes **yummy**.

Have you guessed what it could be?
Look below and you will see,
It is...

Answer: Sweet popcorn.

Siene Marlow McGarry (4)
The Coppice Primary School, Hollywood

Levi's First Riddle

What could it be?
Follow the clues and see.

It looks like **Daddy's head.**
It sounds like **a duck.**
It smells like **a cat.**
It feels **soft like a broom.**
It tastes like **a peanut.**

Have you guessed what it could be?
Look below and you will see,
It is...

Answer: A dog.

Levi Collett (4)
The Coppice Primary School, Hollywood

Ellie's First Riddle

What could it be?
Follow the clues and see.

It looks like **the sky.**
It sounds like **the inside of a shell.**
It smells like **fish.**
It feels like **water.**
It tastes like **salt.**

Have you guessed what it could be?
Look below and you will see,
It is...

Answer: The sea.

Ellie Ryan (5)
The Coppice Primary School, Hollywood

Aaron's First Riddle

What could it be?
Follow the clues and see.

It looks like **snow**.
It sounds like **nothing**.
It smells like **banana and milk**.
It feels **cold**.
It tastes like **chocolate**.

Have you guessed what it could be?
Look below and you will see,
It is...

Answer: Milkshake.

Aaron Brittain (4)
The Coppice Primary School, Hollywood

Kesia's First Riddle

What could it be?
Follow the clues and see.

It looks **green, black or brown.**
It sounds like **a letter.**
It smells like **a flower.**
It feels **hot.**
It tastes like **herbs.**

Have you guessed what it could be?
Look below and you will see,
It is...

Answer: Tea.

Kesia Quaintance (5)
The Coppice Primary School, Hollywood

Eliana's First Riddle

What could it be?
Follow the clues and see.

It looks like **a neck**.
It sounds like **ripping**.
It smells **fresh**.
It feels **smooth**.
It tastes like **flavoured milk**.

Have you guessed what it could be?
Look below and you will see,
It is...

Answer: A banana.

Eliana (4)
The Coppice Primary School, Hollywood

Emily's First Riddle

What could it be?
Follow the clues and see.

It looks **pink and fluffy**.
It sounds **quiet**.
It smells like **custard**.
It feels **soft**.
It tastes **nice**.

Have you guessed what it could be?
Look below and you will see,
It is...

Answer: A teddy.

Emily Astle (4)
The Coppice Primary School, Hollywood

Rozie's First Riddle

What could it be?
Follow the clues and see.

It looks like **a ball**.
It sounds **juicy**.
It smells **fruity**.
It feels **bumpy**.
It tastes **sweet**.

Have you guessed what it could be?
Look below and you will see,
It is...

Answer: An orange.

Rozie Walsh (4)
The Coppice Primary School, Hollywood

Jaxon's First Riddle

What could it be?
Follow the clues and see.

It **has a red face and blonde hair.**
It sounds like ***ooo-ooo-aaah-aaah!***
It smells like **dirt.**
It feels **furry.**
It tastes like **nothing - you can't eat it!**

Have you guessed what it could be?
Look below and you will see,
It is...

Answer: A red-faced monkey.

Jaxon Palmer (5)
The Richard Heathcote Community Primary School,
Alsagers Bank

Sophia's First Riddle

What could it be?
Follow the clues and see.

It **has black stripes and is orange and white.**
It sounds like *roarrr!*
It smells like **a zoo.**
It feels **soft and hairy.**
It tastes like **nothing because you can't eat one**.

Have you guessed what it could be?
Look below and you will see,
It is...

Answer: A *tiger.*

Sophia Stocks (5)
The Richard Heathcote Community Primary School,
Alsagers Bank

Thomas' First Riddle

What could it be?
Follow the clues and see.

It looks **big, black and hairy**.
It sounds like **ooo-ooo-aaah-aaah and beats its chest**.
It smells like **the jungle**.
It feels **furry and soft**.
It **has no taste**.

Have you guessed what it could be?
Look below and you will see,
It is...

Answer: A gorilla.

Thomas Henri Tully (5)
The Richard Heathcote Community Primary School, Alsagers Bank

Arthur's First Riddle

What could it be?
Follow the clues and see.

It looks **brown**.
It sounds like ***ooo-aaah!***
It smells like **the jungle**.
It feels **soft**.
It tastes like **bones**.

Have you guessed what it could be?
Look below and you will see,
It is...

Answer: A monkey.

Arthur Elkington (4)
The Richard Heathcote Community Primary School,
Alsagers Bank

Erin's First Riddle

What could it be?
Follow the clues and see.

It looks like **balls of fur.**
It sounds like *meow!*
It smells like **cat biscuits.**
It feels like **fur.**
It tastes like... **you cannot eat it!**

Have you guessed what it could be?
Look below and you will see,
It is...

Answer: A cat.

Erin Inglis (5)
The Richard Heathcote Community Primary School,
Alsagers Bank

Sebastian's First Riddle

What could it be?
Follow the clues and see.

It looks **stripy and orange and black**.
It sounds like **a lion**.
It smells like **smelly fish**.
It feels **soft and furry**.
It tastes like **fur**.

Have you guessed what it could be?
Look below and you will see,
It is...

Answer: A tiger.

Sebastian Bowers (5)
The Richard Heathcote Community Primary School,
Alsagers Bank

Chad's First Riddle

What could it be?
Follow the clues and see.

It **has colourful feathers and a beak**.
It sounds like **it can talk**.
It **doesn't have a smell**.
It feels **soft**.
It **can't be eaten**.

Have you guessed what it could be?
Look below and you will see,
It is...

Answer: A parrot.

Chad Dubiel-Webster (5)
The Richard Heathcote Community Primary School,
Alsagers Bank

Mia's First Riddle

What could it be?
Follow the clues and see.

It looks like **fur**.
It sounds like ***woof woof***!
It smells like **wet fur**.
It feels **fluffy**.
It tastes like **dog food**.

Have you guessed what it could be?
Look below and you will see,
It is...

Answer: A dog.

Mia Clare Reader (4)
The Richard Heathcote Community Primary School,
Alsagers Bank

Luke's First Riddle

What could it be?
Follow the clues and see.

It looks **black and white**.
It sounds like *thud thud*!
It smells like **bamboo**.
It feels **soft**.
It tastes **dirty**.

Have you guessed what it could be?
Look below and you will see,
It is...

Answer: A panda.

Luke Mottram (4)

The Richard Heathcote Community Primary School,
Alsagers Bank

George's First Riddle

What could it be?
Follow the clues and see.

It looks **fluffy**.
It sounds like **a burp**.
It smells **fresh**.
It feels **soft**.
It tastes like... **you can't eat it**.

Have you guessed what it could be?
Look below and you will see,
It is...

Answer: A dog.

George Hewitt (4)
The Richard Heathcote Community Primary School,
Alsagers Bank

Lillie-Mae's First Riddle

What could it be?
Follow the clues and see.

It **is red with green leaves.**
It **has crunchy seeds.**
It smells **sweet.**
It feels **soft.**
It tastes **delicious.**

Have you guessed what it could be?
Look below and you will see,
It is...

Answer: A strawberry.

Lillie-Mae Latham (4)

The Richard Heathcote Community Primary School,
Alsagers Bank

Leon's First Riddle

What could it be?
Follow the clues and see.

It looks **orange**.
It sounds **crunchy**.
It smells like **soil**.
It feels **hard**.
It tastes like **a vegetable**.

Have you guessed what it could be?
Look below and you will see,
It is...

Answer: A carrot.

Leon Maziarz (4)
The Richard Heathcote Community Primary School,
Alsagers Bank

Anabelle's First Riddle

What could it be?
Follow the clues and see.

It looks like **a black and white bird**.
It sounds like **a gentle voice**.
It smells like **coral reef**.
It feels like **a smooth balloon**.
It tastes like **soft bends**.

Have you guessed what it could be?
Look below and you will see,
It is...

Answer: A killer whale.

Anabelle Grace Pigott (5)
Tudor Grange Primary Academy Haselor, Haselor

Harriet's First Riddle

What could it be?
Follow the clues and see.

It looks like **a bumpy shell**.
It sounds like **calm music**.
It smells like **salty sea**.
It feels like **a soft bed**.
It tastes like **a crunchy apple**.

Have you guessed what it could be?
Look below and you will see,
It is...

Answer: A seahorse.

Harriet Smith (4)
Tudor Grange Primary Academy Haselor, Haselor

Elysia's First Riddle

What could it be?
Follow the clues and see.

It looks like **a curly caterpillar.**
It sounds like **the wind.**
It smells like **sunflowers.**
It feels like **a mermaid's tail.**
It tastes like **the sea.**

Have you guessed what it could be?
Look below and you will see,
It is...

Answer: A seahorse.

Elysia Mabel Pigott (5)
Tudor Grange Primary Academy Haselor, Haselor

Poppy's First Riddle

What could it be?
Follow the clues and see.

It looks like **bumpy rocks**.
It sounds like **swaying seaweed**.
It smells like **slime**.
It feels like **a soft toy**.
It tastes like **a crunchy shell**.

Have you guessed what it could be?
Look below and you will see,
It is...

Answer: A turtle.

Poppy West (5)
Tudor Grange Primary Academy Haselor, Haselor

Téo's First Riddle

What could it be?
Follow the clues and see.

It looks like **a sparkly sun**.
It sounds like **bubbles**.
It smells like **a rubbish bin**.
It feels like **smooth scales**.
It tastes like **the sea**.

Have you guessed what it could be?
Look below and you will see,
It is...

Answer: A blue fish.

Téo Kirby (4)
Tudor Grange Primary Academy Haselor, Haselor

Archer's First Riddle

What could it be?
Follow the clues and see.

It looks like **a sneaky ghost**.
It sounds like **a python**.
It smells like **fish bones**.
It feels like **soft skin**.
It tastes like **fish meat**.

Have you guessed what it could be?
Look below and you will see,
It is...

Answer: A tiger shark.

Archer Fricker (5)
Tudor Grange Primary Academy Haselor, Haselor

144

Spencer's First Riddle

What could it be?
Follow the clues and see.

It looks like **a stripy zebra**.
It sounds like **snow falling**.
It smells like **raw meat**.
It feels like **soft felt**.
It tastes like **pasta**.

Have you guessed what it could be?
Look below and you will see,
It is...

Answer: A striped shark.

Spencer Sandland (5)
Tudor Grange Primary Academy Haselor, Haselor

Nancy's First Riddle

What could it be?
Follow the clues and see.

It looks like **an apple pie**.
It sounds like **castanets**.
It smells like **shells**.
It feels like **a bumpy bottle**.
It tastes like **a crunchy rock**.

Have you guessed what it could be?
Look below and you will see,
It is...

Answer: A crab.

Nancy Devonshire (4)
Tudor Grange Primary Academy Haselor, Haselor

Sebastian's First Riddle

What could it be?
Follow the clues and see.

It looks **as big as a bus**.
It sounds like **an aeroplane**.
It smells like **saltwater**.
It feels like **a hard wall**.
It tastes like **salt**.

Have you guessed what it could be?
Look below and you will see,
It is...

Answer: A killer whale.

Sebastian New (5)
Tudor Grange Primary Academy Haselor, Haselor

Cameron's First Riddle

What could it be?
Follow the clues and see.

It looks like **tree leaves**.
It sounds like **the sea**.
It smells like **snail slime**.
It feels like **a hard shell**.
It tastes like **slugs**.

Have you guessed what it could be?
Look below and you will see,
It is...

Answer: A turtle.

Cameron Bower-Smith (5)
Tudor Grange Primary Academy Haselor, Haselor

Archer's First Riddle

What could it be?
Follow the clues and see.

It looks like **a rope**.
It sounds like **bubbles**.
It smells like **salty sea**.
It feels like **a soft crayon**.
It tastes like **fish**.

Have you guessed what it could be?
Look below and you will see,
It is...

Answer: A stingray.

Archer Charlie Thomas Eftichiou (4)
Tudor Grange Primary Academy Haselor, Haselor

Ewan's First Riddle

What could it be?
Follow the clues and see.

It looks like **a sword**.
It sounds like **swishing**.
It smells like **shells**.
It feels like **smooth grass**.
It tastes like **salt**.

Have you guessed what it could be?
Look below and you will see,
It is...

Answer: A **swordfish**.

Ewan Sloan (4)
Tudor Grange Primary Academy Haselor, Haselor

Poppy's First Riddle

What could it be?
Follow the clues and see.

It looks like **a green tree**.
It sounds like **whispering**.
It smells like **mud**.
It feels **bumpy**.
It tastes like **grass**.

Have you guessed what it could be?
Look below and you will see,
It is...

Answer: A turtle.

Poppy Long (4)
Tudor Grange Primary Academy Haselor, Haselor

Beau's First Riddle

What could it be?
Follow the clues and see.

It looks like **a slithery snake**.
It sounds **squeaky**.
It smells like **salty sea**.
It feels like **a soft blanket**.

Have you guessed what it could be?
Look below and you will see,
It is...

Answer: A dolphin.

Beau Desmond (4)
Tudor Grange Primary Academy Haselor, Haselor

Young Writers Est. 1991

YOUNG WRITERS INFORMATION

We hope you have enjoyed reading this book – and that you will continue to in the coming years.

If you're a young writer who enjoys reading and creative writing, or the parent of an enthusiastic poet or story writer, do visit our website **www.youngwriters.co.uk**. Here you will find free competitions, workshops and games, as well as recommended reads, a poetry glossary and our blog. There's lots to keep budding writers motivated to write!

If you would like to order further copies of this book, or any of our other titles, then please give us a call or order via your online account.

Young Writers
Remus House
Coltsfoot Drive
Peterborough
PE2 9BF
(01733) 890066
info@youngwriters.co.uk

Join in the conversation!
Tips, news, giveaways and much more!

 **YoungWritersUK**    **@YoungWritersCW**